Romantic Relationships in Recovery

John S. Baudhuin, M.A.

CompCare® Publishers

2415 Annapolis Lane
Minneapolis, Minnesota 55441

Library of Congress Cataloging-in-Publication Data

Baudhuin, John.
   Romantic relationships in recovery : resisting the dangers of the 13th step / John S. Baudhuin.
      p. cm.
      ISBN 0-89638-247-8
      1. Compulsive behavior—Patients—Rehabilitation. 2. Interpersonal relations. 3. Twelve-step programs. I. Title. II. Title: 13th step. III. Title: Thirteenth step.
RC533.B27 1991
616.85'227—dc20   91-22800
                                                                                          CIP

Cover design by Jeremy Gale.
Interior design by Lois Stanfield.

Inquiries, orders, and catalog requests should be addressed to:
CompCare Publishers
2415 Annapolis Lane
Minneapolis, Minnesota 55441
612/559-4800 or toll free 800/328-3330

96   95   94   93   92   91
 6   5   4   3   2   1

Contents

Thanks

To Chris F. and Chuck H. for their guidance regarding Twelve Step Programs, to Barbara C. for her colorful vignettes and her own adventures in recovery, to Charlie G. for his enthusiasm, kind words, and inspiration, and of course, to Lucy R. for her constant guidance during this entire project.

And finally to Ruth Mary, whose thoughts, feelings, and spiritual guidance made everything possible.

Author's Preface

It's done. What started out as one of my concerns over the years as a counselor, and then later as a program director, has turned into a book. The clinical information comes from my experience with over 1,500 clients, their families, and recovering people in several states, who bravely shared their experience, strength, and hope about relationship problems in recovery.

The Thirteenth Step is not about any or all relationships that happen in the recovery process. The Thirteenth Step is about exploitation and *harm done in the name of the recovery process*. The concept began in recovery groups when talking about the classic romancer who uses the Twelve Step programs to recruit the young and naive. But in a way, it also applies to clinicians who take advantage of the power role to exploit, and lawyers, professors, and high-powered business people who do the same.

There is no intent to condemn, blame, or produce guilt about any particular relationship. There is no suggestion to anyone that he or she should start, end, or alter a relationship in any way. Those are personal decisions which are, frankly, none of my business. Certainly some may read this and perhaps base some decisions on the information provided. But nowhere at any time does this book tell anyone to do anything more than to take stock and to avoid harming or being harmed.

The ultimate goal of this book is simply to inform and to advance the recovery process. If any of that happens, even for one person, I will consider this a success. Thanks.

Introduction

Janice was free for the first time in her life—free from the desire to drink or use other drugs, free from her parents, free from her physically abusive ex-husband, and now even free from treatment. She hit the local AA scene with great enthusiasm, doing the "90-90" plan (ninety meetings in ninety days) suggested by both her treatment counselor and her AA sponsor. Having been cautioned not to get into a relationship right away, Janice turned down even the most innocent invitations to AA functions and other activities.

George was free too. His wife had rather unceremoniously changed the locks on the house one day, and in just a few weeks they were divorced. His sponsor and AA home group helped him through the crisis, gently reminding him that his Step Ten personal inventory work should include dealing with the womanizing that led to his divorce. Like Janice, he was warned about new relationships, but he was angry and lonely, so he rationalized that some "dating" would be acceptable—as long as he didn't get "too involved."

They noticed each other immediately at the AA Intergroup picnic. George went regularly to the Saturday Niters, a late-night meeting in Treasure Beach. Janice told her sponsor that she needed to try new meetings, and she went, of course, to the Saturday Niters. When the request went out for volunteers to help with the group's anniversary dinner, and Janice noticed George's hand going up, so did hers.

No one, they thought, could possibly guess that they had found one another. They knew it was too soon for both of them, that their sponsors would be very concerned, but the relationship was so perfect, so special. They both liked the Grateful Dead, they were both originally from Pennsylvania, and most important, they both felt lonely, vulnerable, and incomplete.

They decided to attend other AA meetings because of their discomfort. Then, because they were so close and both in recovery, they rationalized that they need not attend so many meetings after all. They didn't see their sponsors as often, but they began to believe that they could, in part, sponsor each other.

When George thought Jan began to seem distant and strange, he was absolutely right. She had started on the pills again and was also drinking an "occasional" glass of wine. Distraught and riddled with guilt, he enlisted the help of AA friends to get Janice into a detoxification center.

That was the end of the relationship. Fortunately, it was also the beginning of their recoveries.

Another story

Mick and Cecelia had both made it through the usual early slings and arrows of recovery from alcoholism and cocaine addiction. And they had almost made some of the usual relationship mistakes. Mick's sponsor, Jim, had guided him along by sharing his own experiences and giving gentle suggestions. Cecelia, on the other hand, got the message more directly in the long-term women's program she was fortunate enough to find. "If you meet some guy you really like and all the fireworks go off," the counselor would say in her lecture on relationships, "for God's sake, run!" Cecelia had a sponsor like Mick's: she never scolded, never lectured, yet never gave up.

Three years along, Mick met Cecelia at a planning meeting for the annual AA picnic. She had been in the AA Program nearly that long. They became friends, and as these things develop, companions. About a year later, they stood proudly in front of a recovering clergyman and recited their wedding vows.

Mick and Cecelia had their problems, individually and as a couple. But one problem they did *not* have was maintaining their separate recovery programs, even as they shared their recoveries with one another.

What's the difference between these two stories? The Thirteenth Step. Jan and George were caught in a Step Thirteen situation. Both tried to fill their emptiness with romance, and to take their recoveries *from* each other. On the other hand, Mick and Cecelia already had full lives, and they brought their recoveries to one another as a very special wedding gift. They had avoided the hazards of the Thirteenth Step. The difference was Step Thirteen.

The purpose of this book, very simply, is to discuss that difference in detail.

No one knows the source of the term "Thirteenth Step." When it's used in AA there are knowing looks and smiles, along with a good deal of denial. Yet there are countless stories of destructive relationships happening at the wrong place and the wrong time with the wrong people. This is a very serious issue in early recovery, and at any other time when people become vulnerable or find themselves adrift, as was the case with George.

Of course, the Thirteenth Step is not official. But if it were actually written down, it might look like this:

Had a passionate and exciting affair with someone in the Program, and one or both relapsed.

This unofficial step refers to what happens when people, knowingly or unknowingly, substitute romance and sex for recovery, when a relationship is used almost like alcohol or other drugs. It is also what happens when a sponsor or otherwise "older" AA member uses the Program to take advantage of a vulnerable newer member.

Step Thirteen blunts the recovery process at its most vulnerable time, reignites codependency concerns, and takes people out of their programs. These quick-fix romances and instant love affairs almost always lead to disastrous results, including full relapses into alcohol or other drug use, violence, and even suicide.

This book will explain the dynamics of relationships as they relate to addiction recovery, offer some precautions about and solutions to Thirteenth Step situations, and give hope to those who still aspire to a viable and rewarding relationship. Most of the Twelve Step Program references are to Alcoholics Anonymous, but the ideas apply equally well to other Twelve Step Programs such as Narcotics Anonymous, Cocaine Anonymous, Overeaters Anonymous, Codependents Anonymous, Sex Addicts Anonymous, Al-Anon Family Groups, and many others.

Part One

Romantic Relationships in Recovery

Chapter 1
Relationships—"We Need the Eggs"

Relationship: a specified state of affairs existing among people related to or dealing with one another.
—*The American Heritage Dictionary,* Second College Edition, 1985

At the end of the film *Annie Hall* (MGM/United Artists, 1977), Woody Allen and Annie break up, creating great pain for both. Woody sadly concludes his aside narrative of their relationship by telling a joke about a man who sees a psychiatrist with the complaint that his brother thinks he is a chicken. The psychiatrist advises the man to avoid the deranged brother completely. The man tells the psychiatrist that he would avoid his brother, but he needs the eggs. When it comes to relationships, Woody Allen muses, they may drive us crazy, but we stay in them because, in spite of the pitfalls and problems, we need them. As he says, "We need the eggs."

The following is a look at relationships in general (excluding family)—an explanation of what kind of "eggs" are available in the first place. Each of these relationships can be applied to an AA situation.

STRANGER

These are brief encounters—for example, a casual conversation with a fellow passenger on a plane, train, or bus. They are entirely based on propinquity—the simple fact of being in the same place at the same time. They end when the journey is over, or sometimes even sooner.

ACQUAINTANCE

These people are known at least by name, having been introduced at some function or event. There is ongoing contact only if we happen to meet them again. People who sometimes attend the same AA meeting would fit this category.

COWORKER/COLLEAGUE/NEIGHBOR

When some ongoing circumstance, like work, a special volunteer project, or living in the same immediate area keeps us together, a relationship may develop based on that circumstance. Conversation is usually limited to discussing the boss, a new car or computer, the supermarket, the PTA, or other things related to the mutual situation. When the job, school, or neighborhood changes, the relationship ends.

FRIEND

Friendships may start with one of the earlier relationships, but now the people seek out one another beyond that situation. For example, he changes jobs, but he still bowls with the guys from his former office. She moves downtown, but she still volunteers at the hospital in the suburbs with her former neighbor. Friends may disappear for a time, but when they return, it soon seems as if they had never left. Friends care and are willing to do many things to help one another. Most of us have many acquaintances and associates, but are lucky to have even a few true friends.

COMPANION

A companion is a good friend who becomes a part of someone's life. A companion is someone with whom one might travel, spend vacations, even live. A companion is a person not just to do things with, but to *be* with; a companion can be told almost anything without risk of ending the friendship. People in successful marriages say it's the companionship

4

that counts the most.

AA members, particularly those with good sobriety, tend to find companions who are also in AA. AA sponsorship relationships often turn into companionship over time.

BOYFRIEND/GIRLFRIEND

Exclusive relationships with some romantic and sexual involvement belong here. In modern times, these couples often live together, and many operate similar to marriage. The difference? "We're together for *now*." There is exclusivity without an official or even an unspoken long-term commitment.

MATE/LOVER

A marriage or a committed live-in situation fits here. Most therapists strongly believe that we must walk through the first levels of relating if this one is to even have a chance.

There are many "Program marriages" (when both people are in AA or other Twelve Step Programs). Some appear to work very well, and some do not. Reasons for both outcomes will become apparent in this book. If a married person joins AA and the spouse does not join Al-Anon or have other equivalent therapy, the marriage may founder as their interests and spirituality change.

Herb, for example, was not even alcoholic when he married Kristin, but he quickly crossed the line into the early years of the disease. A few years and two kids later, he was in big trouble with his drinking. His company intervened. Fortunately, Herb was enthusiastic about recovery almost at once. Kristin, on the other hand, was emotionally shut down and very suspicious of Herb's sudden recovery. Her parents had died from the effects of alcoholism. She refused to participate in "Family Week" at his treatment program, and she did not attend Al-Anon later. Kristin had been able to cope with Herb's drinking, but she could not handle his recovery.

They continued to drift apart until Herb left the marriage; he had just celebrated his third year of sobriety.

Most people still want the "mate/lover" relationship. Many rationalize the pain of not being in a relationship, or of being in a bad one, by either joking about it or giving long speeches about the value of being unattached. Certainly much can be learned from being alone, and certainly not everyone needs to be in a committed relationship, but the mate/lover relationship still is a goal or a hope for most. And, should one happen, people should be aware of how affairs develop, from that first romantic blast-off to that later, quieter serenity.

The next chapter describes the three phases of romantic love relationships. These phases may or may not take place within the context of the seven kinds of relationships just described.

Chapter 2
Phases of Romantic Love Relationships

I didn't know what hit me. I'd meet him on trains, planes, and ships at sea, anywhere he wanted. And he was married!

—*Texas AA member*

We were no longer singing from the same hymnal.

—*Pittsburgh AA member*

THE INITIAL HIGH

A romantic relationship often begins with the realization that someone is becoming "special." An initial romantic high usually follows. Since the beginning of expressive arts, romances have been a steady feature of poetry, novels, and films.

The romantic high, however special and even "spiritual" the lovers believe it to be, may also have some chemical components. Psychotherapists Klein and Libowitz suggested in an April 1980 *Ms.* magazine article that when a person is "in love," the brain may secrete an amphetamine-like substance called phenylethylamine. This substance suppresses appetite and sleep and produces a euphoria that seriously impairs judgment. At this stage of the relationship, the loved one can do no wrong, and no matter what others say or how inappropriate the circumstances might be, the lovers will sing the glories of their relationship. Attempts to conceal their feelings for one another usually fail; others sense the "vibes" from far away.

Patrick Carnes, Ph.D., a nationally recognized authority on

sex addiction, and author of *Out of the Shadows, A Gentle Path Through the Twelve Steps, Don't Call It Love,* and *Contrary to Love,* stated at a Florida seminar in July 1990 that romance and sex addiction have a "neurochemical base" in phenylethylamine. He said that this substance is secreted most powerfully in the early stages of a relationship, and that when the effect fades, the person may look to other sources to sustain the "high."

Therapist Susan Page, in her book *If I'm So Wonderful, Why Am I Still Single?* adds that when "the infatuation ends, the thwarted lover's brain stops production of the 'upper,' and the resulting pain . . . is like drug withdrawal." Page speculates that since chocolate is also believed to contain phenylethylamine, that may explain why the stereotypical rejected Hollywood lover so often munched from a large box of bonbons. Dr. Carnes, on the other hand, believes that ingested phenylethylamine does not reach the bloodstream at sufficient levels for this effect.

In his book *The Road Less Traveled,* M. Scott Peck, M.D., describes the romantic experience as a "sudden collapse of ego boundaries." We willingly subject ourselves to every whim of the other person, and, because our identity is totally absorbed, we can see no cause for conflict or disharmony. This helps to explain why many couples in an initial romantic high wonder why anyone in love could ever have an argument!

The romantic high can be a beautiful experience. For some, it occurs once in a lifetime; for others, it never happens; most of us experience it more than once. Few romances occur at exactly the right time and circumstances, and we really can't "plan" them or force them to happen. Dr. Peck suggests that if a romance does happen under totally impossible circumstances, we need only be patient. The feelings will soon pass.

Newcomers to AA are particularly susceptible to being carried away by an initial romantic high because, as anyone in the Program will tell you, they cannot think clearly about *anything,* let alone a new love interest.

The denial and evasiveness that accompany the Thirteenth Step have inspired many colorful terms among AA members to clarify the concept. For instance, a popular downstate Illinois expression is "No he-ing or she-ing." A North Carolina phrase is "No pairing off." On Long Island, it's "the boys with the boys and the girls with the girls." Despite slogans and the clarity of the "rules," the Thirteenth Step continues to be a problem.

The initial romantic high is also dangerous if one or both people have serious problems with codependency. When such partners try to write scripts about their romance—to control each other and force outcomes—tremendous problems can ensue. Janice and George discovered this. They were both intelligent and sensible about other things, yet they lost their good sense about their romance.

THE CONFLICT PHASE

The biochemical aspects of romance do pass. Always. This does not mean that a couple no longer experiences romance. A romantic spark still glows for many people who have been together for decades. But that initial high does fade, followed by a return to the previous ego boundaries, a retreat to the safety of self. No matter how wonderful the romance, most lovers will seek to reestablish their identities, unless they are markedly codependent.

The couple begins to notice things that were blurred by the romantic high. He is *always* late. She hangs nylon pantyhose out to dry on every elevation in the county. He wears the same shirt all weekend. She's *always* on the phone with her mother. And—can you believe this—he sent a birthday card to his *ex*-wife! His kids come for weekends and aren't quite as cute as they used to be. Her neurotic dog sheds and cries half the night. This is conflict time, when normal individual preferences, habits, and differences emerge from the romantic medication.

The conflict phase is often where the romance ends. And with recovering alcoholics, especially when one or both are relatively new to the AA Program, this ending too often leads to another ending: a drink or other drug. The AA World Services book, *Living Sober*, notes on page 62 that making our sobriety contingent on another's sobriety "proves flatly disastrous...We have to stay sober for ourselves, no matter what other people do or fail to do." The book also points out that intense attraction can quickly turn into intense dislike, which can be equally entangling.

THE ACCEPTANCE PHASE

With a little bit of luck, a lot of hard work, and true commitment, two can survive the conflict stage and actually grow from it. The beauty of the acceptance phase is not "I love you because..." but "I love you in spite of..." Contrary to the popular expression that love conquers all, it does not. But, with some willingness and hard work, love *can* survive. It may not always lead us to climb the tallest mountain, but it could keep us from leaping off the nearest cliff.

Good relationships contain elements of all those other, less intense relationships. If we have only the initial fireworks of romance, and do not become friends and companions, the relationship probably will not survive the inevitable conflict stage. In a codependent relationship where one partner is often highly submissive, the relationship may actually last a little—or a *lot*—longer. But even here, the outcome usually is painful. AA couples, indeed all couples, could well look at the kinds of relationships listed in Chapter 1 and take stock of where they are now—for instance, as friends—before they evaluate every small detail of their sex lives or other sensitive issues.

Chapter 3
Romance and Recovery: What Can Go Wrong

If we examine every disturbance we have, great or small, we will find at the root of it some unhealthy dependency and its consequent unhealthy demand.

—Bill W., in the January 1958 *Grapevine;* reprinted in *The AA Way of Life,* p. 288.

Early recovery from alcoholism or any other kind of drug addiction is fraught with perils. It is a time when many "float" between denial and acceptance, reality and fantasy. On any given day, newly recovering people can be highly motivated for recovery, grateful to be in recovery, and very close to their AA friends. But it takes so little to upset that state: an unwanted tone of voice from a lover on the telephone, or no telephone call at all; a love letter, or no letter when one has been promised, or even a "Dear John" letter. Other things that rock the recovery boat can be as simple as a negative remark at a Twelve Step meeting, a bad day in group therapy, or a parking ticket. The newly recovering person stands with one foot on the dock and one in the boat. The results can be tragic, as in the following example.

A Florida AA member told of a new sponsee who telephoned her in the middle of the night in a state of hysteria. The young woman had shared her despondent feelings that evening at her AA meeting, and had then accepted a ride home and some emotional support from a man in the group who seemed very sympathetic. When they reached her apartment, he made forceful sexual overtures. She rejected him immediately, but she was emotionally devastated. Her sponsor called *his* sponsor to block any further contact between them. Unfortunately, it was too late for this fragile newcomer: two days after this incident, she took her life.

Certain vital things must occur in order for recovery to take hold, and a romantic situation or highly stressful co-dependent relationship can prevent these growth phases from developing. For instance, recovering people need to bond with the recovery program and with other recovering people. That's why many advise the newcomer to do the "90-90" plan, also known as "90 in 90," which means attending one or more AA meetings each day for the first ninety days. This practice puts recovery first, one day at a time, creates numerous opportunities to meet and socialize with other recovering people, and greatly increases the chances of finding appropriate AA groups and a good AA sponsor. A new romance during this time will often destroy the entire process.

Once I was with him, everything else went out the window. I went to meetings in a daze, often not even remembering who led.

—New York City AA member.

The Program is just as important as the fellowship itself. Newcomers need to actually "work" the Twelve Steps, one at a time, with a sponsor's guidance. The difficult intellectual and emotional process of working the Steps requires concentration and dedication; again, this becomes very difficult if a romantic attraction interferes. AA's "Big Book" suggests on page 58 that the Step work is difficult, and that "at some of these we balked. We thought we could find an easier, softer way."

It's difficult to know which Step you're on when you're in bed.

—Florida AA member.

A Program relationship can be beautiful, but only if the people truly *have* a program. Recall that in romantic love, one ego collapses into another. If the partners have not yet developed their own sense of self, which is true in early recovery, they simply may not survive the power of the new relationship. It is no accident that people make the same relationship mistakes again and again. If they take no time to learn about themselves after the last mistake, they will always return to the familiar.

The romantic high carries with it a biochemical *and* psychological high. Therapist and writer Frank Pittman wrote in the April 1990 *New Woman* magazine that a romance can be "an intense, passionate alliance that...closes out other reality." He added that "falling in love is much like a manic episode." And what usually follows the manic part is a "crash," leading to a craving for more, just as with cocaine addiction. Thus a romantic high can become another "drug" to be sought. The person cannot bond with the Fellowship, cannot work the Steps, and cannot develop a sense of self. Improvement in recovery stops.

One frightening risk to AA members in a romantic entanglement is the concurrent lack of judgment. Two counselors, Jim and Donna, were both married, worked for the same treatment center, and were recovering alcoholics. They believed themselves to be in love. Jim, it was later discovered, had lied about the length of his sobriety when he applied for his job there—he had only a few months, not the required two years. When the center's director attempted to inform them, separately, about the dangers of their relationship, Donna replied with a blissful smile, "You just don't understand, do you? This is a *spiritual* relationship! God wants me to be with Jim." The director told Donna that despite what God might want, *he* wanted the romance ended; it was a matter of common sense as well as hospital policy, which had been explained to both counselors during their orientations. The relationship ended quickly when Jim got the news. He wanted to keep his job! Donna, on the other hand, continued her relationship pathology: she moved a recently "graduated" patient into her apartment, and was then dismissed from her counseling job at that facility. She took the former patient with her to California, where he promptly relapsed. They then separated to points unknown.

Relationships are spiritual. They can be a great gift from God or the "Higher Power." It is no wonder that people in early recovery, or others with serious relationship problems, including codependency, may confuse the manic aspects of a romance with a true spiritual encounter. Perhaps the two are not that different. Healthy relationships have a powerful spiritual base, but they are also based firmly on planet Earth. As St. Paul wrote in 1 Corinthians, 13.4, "Love is patient and kind." This means that a healthy relationship can have a great deal of glitter and excitement, but will also sustain a peace and calmness.

ROMANCE ADDICTION

The addictive nature of a romance's biochemical aspects can cause some people to become "hooked" on having new romantic experiences. One relatively new Twelve Step group, Sex and Love Addicts Anonymous (SLAA), was founded to help these people. A good illustration of the power of this addiction is a story in the SLAA "Big Book" about a man who had an affair while on his honeymoon! What he was after was not just the sex, but the excitement of the new conquest. Mozart's great opera, *Don Giovanni*, is about the legendary Don Juan, who had a scroll filled with the names of his romantic conquests.

So this problem is not new, but it is particularly dangerous for recovering alcoholics. Romance addiction demands constant attention to the details of the last relationship and preoccupation about the next one. There is no time or stability for the kind of spiritual growth needed for high-quality recovery from chemical dependency.

A WORD ABOUT SEX ADDICTION

Patrick Carnes, Ph.D., of the Golden Valley Institute for Behavioral Medicine in Minneapolis, describes sex addiction as a behavioral addiction with some neurochemical involvement. By this he means that part of becoming addicted to certain sexual behaviors involves a dependence on changes in brain chemistry produced by the behavior. We cross the line into addiction, then, when we continue a certain behavior despite harmful consequences to ourselves and to others. An in-depth discussion of sex addiction is not within the scope of this book, but the subject is included because "Thirteenth Steppers" may be involved in a sex addiction.

In his latest book, *Don't Call It Love,* Dr. Carnes writes (on page 35) that 42 percent of the sex addicts involved in his research were *also* chemically dependent. This means that many people recovering from chemical dependency may still be untreated for sex addiction. For example, a well-known manager of an extended care facility in the Midwest had a widely know penchant for "sponsoring" young girls. A respected AA "elder statesman" and author of a book on the Twelve Steps, also from the Midwest, became involved with a young woman of another recovery fellowship. A counselor in a halfway house for young women was involved with at least four clients before his job was terminated. As is so often the case with alcoholism, the "no-talk rule" applied here. Only in the case of the man who was terminated was anything ever done or said about it.

The conspiracy of silence around the Thirteenth Step and sex addiction reflects our great discomfort about these subjects. When AA members and recovery professionals say nothing, the problems only continue, harming both the addicts and those who are used to satisfy their addiction. For example, the man (see page 11) who tried to seduce the newcomer had probably done this many times before. But, until the woman's sponsor confronted his sponsor, nothing had ever been said. Tragically, unless the man sought and received treatment for his sexual behavior, he probably continued his actions, despite his own best intentions to stop.

Two things must happen if things are ever to change: 1) people close to the situation must be willing to break the "no-talk rule"; and 2) those for whom the behavior constitutes yet *another* addiction must get professional help from someone who understands alcoholism *and* sex addiction. (A resources section at the end of this book lists some possibilities for help.)

Even though some people have used Twelve Step Programs to meet unhealthy relationship needs, most often these Programs are a safe and marvelous way to begin and maintain recovery. Recovering people who are insecure about how to evaluate and relate to others on a romantic level can resolve this dilemma by making it a rule to leave AA meetings with a friend and to always attend Program functions with small groups of fellowship members. Newcomers to AA who live alone should be wary of inviting *anyone* of the opposite sex into their homes "unchaperoned."

SEXUAL PROBLEMS

Many recovering people have biological and/or psychological sexual dysfunctions. These may or may not be related to their alcohol or other drug addiction. Some "use" newcomers to the AA Program as mere objects with whom to work out or escape their dysfunctions. Impotence and premature ejaculation are common male sexual problems in early recovery. Many women have trouble with arousal or orgasms.

In both situations, recovering alcoholics may use a new relationship as a proving ground for sexual competence. Still more alarming are those few truly "deviant" individuals who prey on vulnerable newly recovering people to carry out unusual and sometimes very high-risk sexual practices.

It is important to neither overemphasize nor underemphasize sexual dysfunctions. One study reported in *Now about Sex,* John Baudhuin, Hazelden, indicated that many sexual dysfunctions disappear with recovery from chemical dependency, but those that do not will require treatment.

Sexual dysfunctions should be kept in perspective. An AA member from the Southeast, who was experiencing problems with impotence, described himself as "totally dysfunctional with women." He later realized, with the help of a sponsor, that he had a *temporary* biological problem, but that meanwhile he remained very "functional" with women as a friend, companion, and—in most senses of the word—a lover.

ALTERNATIVE SEXUAL PREFERENCES

Nearly all the issues described about the heterosexual alcoholic are quite similar for the homosexual, but there are some differences.

First, the numbers are different. Perhaps less than 10 percent of the general population is homosexual, meaning that the odds of finding the right person for a homosexual relationship are much less than for heterosexuals.

Second, society's attitudes and people's personal beliefs about this subject are highly charged emotionally, which makes it difficult for many parents, siblings, coworkers, and friends to fully understand and accept. This lack of acceptance contributes to the same low self-esteem that can breed Step Thirteen situations. Also, gays and lesbians often must be very careful about revealing their lifestyles for fear of prejudice leading to job loss, or legal and other problems. While "gay bashing" may be less common now than a few decades ago, repeated incidents in areas where there are large gay populations perpetuate that constant fear.

Finally, homosexuals usually cannot celebrate a relationship as heterosexuals can. They think twice about walking hand in hand on the average city street, for example, because of the risk of ridicule or even physical harm.

Socializing can be particularly difficult for the gay or lesbian recovering alcoholics because so much homosexual socializing goes on in bars; recovery can at first seem like self-imposed exile. Fortunately, most larger cities (and even some small towns) now have special-interest AA groups for gays and lesbians.

SEXUAL ABUSE AND CHEMICAL DEPENDENCY RECOVERY

Definitions of sexual abuse vary widely, as do statistics about how often it occurs. In my opinion, sexual abuse is any kind of nonconsenting molestation or other form of sexual intrusion. (In general, minors are regarded as *always* being nonconsenting.) Exposing children to pornography, allowing them to observe overt sexual activity, and drawing undue attention to children's sexual development can also be considered abusive behaviors.

Regardless of these points of definition, the issues leave recovering people extremely vulnerable. At a Florida seminar on August 6, 1990, Dr. Carnes said that for those who must recover from both sexual abuse *and* chemical dependency, the recovery process is placed "on hold" by addictive chemicals. Dr. Carnes suggested a phased abuse recovery process which may take a year or more.

Newly recovering people, whether or not they are sexual abuse victims, have trouble with boundaries and limits. Abuse victims have even more trouble, and are therefore much more vulnerable to predatory Thirteenth Steppers. In fact, a compulsive Thirteenth Stepper may be an untreated sexual abuse victim. An untreated abuse victim still carries a great sense of shame over what happened and literally may not know what is acceptable and what is not, particularly if the abuse took place repeatedly over a long period of time. Not only does Step Thirteen cause the recovery problems already mentioned, but also, for sexual abuse victims, Thirteenth Step relationships can block recovery from the abuse.

Sexual abuse is often so deeply repressed that it doesn't even show until recovery has begun. Alcohol and/or other drugs help to repress the highly painful abuse memories.

Karen was a forty-year-old, married woman with a supportive spouse, Karl, and a good recovery from chemical dependence. But, after a few sober months, she began to have disturbing dreams and withdrew completely from her husband. Karen and Karl had not experienced this much discord even when she drank. In private therapy, she began to remember sexual abuse by an uncle during several of her childhood years. Along with repressing that sexual abuse, Karen had lost most of her other childhood memories. She did extensive therapy on those issues and is now beginning to rebuild her almost shattered marriage to Karl. But, had she not had a supportive spouse, a good AA Program, and professional help, she would likely have returned to drinking.

Many abuse victims feel guilty about what happened, somehow believing that it was their fault. Such mistaken beliefs further contribute to shame and leave the person vulnerable.

OTHER HIGH-RISK TIMES

Any time of vulnerability—a health or job crisis, serious marital or other family problems, moving to a new area, death, or divorce—can lead to Step Thirteen.

Charlie tells an amusing yet unsettling story he calls "My Trip to Switzerland." "I was about seven years sober. I had what I thought was a terrible marriage, and I was really struggling. One day, at the treatment center where I worked, I met a coworker named Sherrie. She was about ten years younger, and her family had more money than God. Before I knew it, the vibes were there, and she wanted to take me to Switzerland, where she had friends and family.

"I went to my AA sponsor for advice. He said that the trip sounded like an interesting idea. Of course, he pointed out that my wife and three kids wouldn't like it; I'd probably get kicked out of the house. And my boss was kind of prudish, so I'd get fired, too. But, what the hell, maybe Sherrie was worth it!

"I sat straight up in bed that night and almost cried out loud, 'My sponsor thinks I shouldn't go to Switzerland!' I suddenly realized how close I'd been to the edge of the abyss. Oh—and Sherrie, well, I heard recently that she went out drinking again. If I'd hooked up with her, it could have been fatal for me."

Some stories are not as quickly resolved as this one. Vulnerable times always require extra vigilance.

ROMANCE IN THERAPY

A final vulnerable area is perhaps the most obvious: the therapeutic relationship. Most state licensing and credentialing boards specifically prohibit counselors and *any* other treatment staff from getting romantically involved with clients. Some have a six-month rule. For others, it is two years or more.

LeClair Bissell, M.D., and James E. Royce, S.J., point out in their book *Ethics for Addiction Professionals* that there are really two issues. First, the obvious concern about social and romantic relationships between staff and patients, and second, the potential problem of AA relationships. "Today's patient in treatment becomes tomorrow's peer in AA." The authors suggest great caution and good judgment in both of these areas.

In a Miami, Florida, ethics workshop on June 6, 1990, addiction consultant William Olcott of Appleton, Wisconsin, stated that staff should *never* have social or other contacts with former patients. At least one internationally known treatment center mandates no business or social contact with a former patient for two years.

Each program and each person will have to design individually appropriate policies, but it remains clear that any exploitation of a therapeutic relationship for romantic, sexual, or business purposes, is categorically wrong. In fact, Olcott says that in some states it is now a felony offense to take sexual advantage of a patient or client.

There are many tragic stories in the addiction treatment field involving counselors, nurses, physicians, and other professionals whose own dysfunctions led them to prey upon the most vulnerable patients or clients. George, a treatment center counselor, fell in love with an airline stewardess, Velma, who was a patient there. George was so smitten by Velma that he forgot, or decided to ignore, the treatment center's rules against relationships with patients. Her "graduation day" from treatment was his day off. He picked up Velma at the center and gave her a ride home—to *his* home! He was fired immediately from that job, and began drinking three weeks later.

Those involved in the Thirteenth Step should not be blamed, but understood; they should not be ostracized, but helped. Most will need a very solid AA Program, and many will need additional therapy, particularly if there are abuse or COA (children of alcoholics) issues.

. . . AND, OF COURSE, CODEPENDENCY

Codependency is variously defined as living through or by the emotions of others, excessive caretaking, enabling, a passive-dependent personality disorder, a passive-aggressive personality disorder, and a borderline personality disorder. Perhaps the following quips about codependency say it best:

21

Question: What happens when a codependent dies?

Answer: Somebody else's life flashes through his or her mind.

or:

Question: What's a relapse for a recovering codependent?

Answer: A fleeting moment of compassion.

Whenever we place our own feelings and needs totally at the whim of the feelings and needs of another person, whenever we gain most of our self-esteem from the success of someone else, whenever we base our life on the life of another, we are probably being codependent. The term came into the treatment field in the early 1970s as chemical dependency professionals recognized the need to address those affected by alcoholism as well as those afflicted by it. Other terms used briefly were "para-alcoholics" and "co-alcoholics," which recognized that people who lived with an alcoholic adopted similar thinking and behavior to that of the alcoholic, but without the drinking or other drug use. It was then a simple step to "codependent" from the new-at-the-time addiction term, "chemically dependent." As the CD field developed, some professionals believed that the term "codependent" was inadequate, and many clinicians rejected it. Nevertheless, until a better word comes along, we will undoubtedly continue to use the term "codependency" to describe enmeshed, passive-dependent relationships.

Step Thirteen would not be possible, or at least not so prevalent, were it not for codependency. Since many, if not most, alcoholics grew up in an alcoholic environment, the likelihood is great that issues of codependency will surface after an alcoholic sobers up. In a theoretical sense, many of us switch addictions from alcohol or other drugs to relationships. And that desperate need to take care of someone leads to great Thirteenth Step vulnerability. It can cause the best of us to make the worst possible decisions, to hang on foolishly in bad situations, and to reject good situations in which we sense that we will not be able to control and manipulate the other person.

It's vital to recognize and get help for codependency as part of the overall recovery process. However, we must also be careful not to get sidetracked into blaming ourselves, our parents, or the next romance. The AA "Big Book" is very clear on this subject, suggesting repeatedly that we must take our own inventory first, not that of others. As we do this, all of our relationship issues, including codependency, will come into perspective and can then be effectively addressed.

The next chapter describes ways to identify, prevent, and treat the Thirteenth Step.

Chapter 4
Preventing the Thirteenth Step

In taking an inventory (Fourth Step), a member might consider questions such as these:

How did my selfish pursuit of the sex relation damage other people and me? What people were hurt, and how badly? Just how did I react at the time? Did I burn with guilt? Or did I insist that I was the pursued and not the pursuer, and thus absolve myself? How have I reacted to frustration in sexual matters? When denied, did I become vengeful or depressed? Did I take it out on other people? If there was rejection or coldness at home, did I use this as a reason for promiscuity?

—Bill W., *The AA Way of Life*, p. 270

THIRTEENTH STEP EXCUSES

TYPICAL:

"He/she understands."

"We're soulmates."

"It's strictly platonic."

"It's okay—he/she is still in another relationship."

"We're just good friends."

"We have a spiritual connection. We're both Presbyterian/Jewish/Catholic/Episcopal/Druid."

"We just have so many interests in common."

"I couldn't find a good female (male) sponsor."

"She/he isn't taking any new pigeons (sponsees)."

"It's just temporary."

"He/she is a friend of the family."

"As long as we don't get involved."

"We keep separate home groups."

"(Name here) is like a father/mother or son/daughter to me."

"(Name here) reminds me of our family priest/ rabbi/doctor/lawyer/television repairman."

"She/he is so vulnerable—I don't want to hurt him/her."

DEFIANT:

"We're *adults*!"

"I know my limits!"

"I'm a big boy/girl now!"

"No one's going to tell *me* who I can sleep with!"

"I had a Catholic/Protestant/Jewish/ Islamic/Buddhist/ Druid upbringing, and they made me feel *so* guilty. Now I can be me!"

"After the way my first wife/husband/librarian/dentist/tire salesman treated me, I'm *entitled* to some fun."

WEST COAST:

"We share an awesome spirituality."

"We're into each other's space."

"It's real radical, I know, but it's just for now."

"Excellent!"

A FIELD GUIDE TO IDENTIFYING
THE THIRTEENTH STEPPER

Although no two human beings are exactly alike in appearance or behavior, nevertheless certain behavioral and appearance cues may assist us to identify the potential Thirteenth Stepper. No one behavior constitutes a positive identification. Just as birds often must be observed in flight by an ornithologist before a positive ID can be made, so must a Thirteenth Stepper be seen in pursuit of his or her quarry.

1. "Advertising" during Discussion Meetings:

"Of course, I'm not in a relationship right now." (hint, hint!)

"My wife/husband/guru and I have been seeing this therapist."

"She/he doesn't understand codependency."

"I really need to be at a meeting tonight . . . he/she doesn't understand that."

"Have you ever felt lonely even in a crowd?"

"My sponsor thinks I need to get out more."

"We just got back from Marriage Encounter."

"She/he hates my car/dog/cat/roller skates."

"It's always better before you get married."

"I think I'm ready for a relationship now." (*to a sponsor*)

"I just really need to be on my own right now."

"Of course, who would have *me,* anyway?"

2. Advertising Outfits and Accessories

Fifty-seven-year-old man or woman stuffed into teenage son's or daughter's ripped, too-tight jeans.

Toupée that looks like it fell from a passing flying squirrel.

Almost totally unbuttoned shirt or blouse, with a tattoo of the battleship Missouri completely visible.

Driving a convertible with the top down in a blizzard or rainstorm.

3. Post-Meeting Moves and Remarks

"I go right by there (Saskatoon, Saskatchewan) on my way to Jersey. Can I give you a ride?"

"Look, it's your birthday/your anniversary/your day you bought the new microwave last year—you shouldn't be alone."

"Just to talk."

"Just to share some thoughts on the Steps/Traditions/ slogans/'Big Book'/disarmament treaty."

"As long as we're going right by my place/your place, we might as well stop in."

Still viable for the elderly set: "Come and see my etchings."

Also for the elderkinder: "My TV is broken—could I catch 'The Golden Girls' this week with you?"

4. Sponsor Warnings:

"He/she is still a little vulnerable."

"He/she has been around."

"Lots of mileage on that one!"

"She/he has round heels."

"He/she needs to work on the Steps some more."

"If you see him/her, I'll _____. (insert appropriate threat)

"Before you do *anything,* call me."

Now, seriously . . .

The previous lists are partly true, partly for fun. Nevertheless, most manipulative or exploitive behavior has a certain classical style that can be recognized by those who are less vulnerable to it, as they come to the aid of the more vulnerable. Many Thirteenth Steppers are obvious from a distance, while others are more subtle. The old adage "Look out for the quiet guy" is more truth than fiction, for frequently the Thirteenth Stepper is a nice, fatherly or motherly person, whose kindliness conceals a need to use people and to be needed in unhealthy ways.

The next chapters will deal more with prevention, suggesting ways that we can either stop a Thirteenth Step relationship before it starts, or end it as quickly as possible if it has begun.

The first and best defense against Step Thirteen is a good recovery program. This includes:

A HOME AA GROUP

Most successfully recovering people belong to at least *one regular* AA group, which meets at least once a week. Attending home group meetings should be a top priority for members.

Members of a home AA group know one another well. Every member is on the membership list (last initial only if preferred), and is encouraged to telephone other members regularly. This is the group to go with when attending AA dinners, picnics, and dances; celebrating AA anniversaries; making dates for lunch, coffee, and ice cream. This is the group to share with completely. Belonging to a home AA group provides a sense of "family" and a safe place to go and grow.

Sage members of a home AA group will notice, and will know how to tactfully nip a Step Thirteen romance in the bud.

A SPONSOR

AA members need sponsors, particularly when they are still quite new in the Program, but later on as well. A sponsee admires the sponsor's sobriety and lifestyle, but there should be little or no likelihood of a Step Thirteen situation. This usually means a same-sex sponsor. It should also mean a sponsor who is *not* involved in Thirteen Stepping!

The AA World Services pamphlet *Questions and Answers on Sponsorship* suggests that men sponsor men, and women sponsor women. This "reduces the likelihood of emotional distractions that might take the newcomer's mind off the purpose of AA." There are some recovering gays or lesbians who may choose an opposite-sex sponsor for the same reason. However, most do well with a sponsor of any lifestyle as long as the sponsor has a solid AA foundation and strong sobriety.

Finding a good sponsor may take some time. Many newcomers choose a "temporary" sponsor until a more permanent choice comes along. AA members should meet with their sponsors frequently, both at AA meetings and other times. Frequent telephone contact, at least daily during a crisis, is also vital. Step work with and through the sponsor also helps build a powerful bond of sharing and growth.

In particular, taking a Fourth and Fifth Step with a sponsor, focusing only on romance and sex, can help to guard against Thirteenth Step involvement. On page 69, AA's "Big Book" says: "We reviewed our own conduct over the years past. Where had we been selfish, dishonest, or inconsiderate? Whom had we hurt? Did we unjustifiably arouse jealousy, suspicion or bitterness? We got this all down on paper and . . . tried to shape a sane and sound ideal for our future sex life. We subjected each relation to this test—was it selfish or not?"

All this protects against a Thirteenth Step situation. Mary, for example, was so accustomed to discussing everything important with her sponsor that, even after four years sober, she seriously considered asking her sponsor to meet with and evaluate a prospective husband for her!

MEN'S AND WOMEN'S AA GROUPS

Recovering alcoholics need to validate who they are and to be in group settings that reinforce who they are, whether gay or straight. Women should attend at least one all-female AA group, and men should attend an all-male group. Same-gender AA groups increase the bonding of male-to-male and female-to-female, and they greatly reduce the Thirteenth Step possibilities. It's not practical or even necessary in AA to totally avoid the opposite sex, but same-gender groups help make people more comfortable with themselves as men and women. And as their comfort levels rise, people become more comfortable with and more objective about the opposite sex.

Many AA women find that they need to learn to like and trust other women. Many men hesitate to confide in other men for fear of seeming vulnerable and losing the "macho" image; they, too, must learn new ways. Same-gender AA groups can help both men and women a great deal.

THE FELLOWSHIP

Page 70 of AA's "Big Book" (*Alcoholics Anonymous*) tells us that when relationship or sexual issues trouble us, AA members should "throw ourselves the harder into helping others." This means volunteering to speak at meetings, to make coffee and set up chairs, to help clean up after meetings, to answer the Intergroup phone, to "Twelfth Step," and to simply enjoy the recovery fellowship. The dinners, dances, coffee klatches, and other activities are usually casual, inexpensive events with lots of people; they are not as threatening as dating. Travel agencies have caught on, too, and now sponsor special recovery events—sober cruises and even special "recovery weeks" and weekends at favorite resorts worldwide.

SPIRITUALITY

Religiosity is for people who don't want to go to Hell. Spirituality is for people who have already been there.

—Connecticut AA member

The best recovery includes a well-developed but growing spiritual program. This does not mean that everyone must become religious. Rather it means striving to find and develop those things which give our lives meaning and purpose. The greater the sense of meaning, purpose, and direction, the less vulnerability there will be to the Thirteenth Step. Spirituality also helps us to overcome past guilt and shame.

Chapter 5
When It's Already Happening

The deception of others is nearly always rooted in the deception of ourselves.
—Bill W., *AA Grapevine*, August 1961; reprinted in *The AA Way of Life*, p. 17

Unfortunately, most AA members don't think much about Step Thirteen until it's already happened, or is about to happen. Following are some guidelines for action if the Thirteenth Step is under way.

THE TALK RULE

For those who wonder if they are entering an inappropriate relationship, this guideline may help: if the relationship cannot be discussed even with close friends, it probably is not a good one.

Jack and Anita, both members, carried on a secret relationship for over a year without telling a soul. (Jack was single, but Anita was married.) The fact they could not share this romance with even their best friends was not only sad, but also an indicator that the relationship was high-risk. One of the great delights of a new romantic relationship is sharing it with friends; this pair could never do that.

So, if one or both cannot tell anybody about it, unless it's a surprise birthday party, it's probably something inappropriate, like a Thirteenth Step.

DON'T LOOK FOR TROUBLE

Perhaps the attraction is still at the fantasy level; no words have been shared. Some mistakenly interpret AA's requirement for honesty to mean that one *must* tell the other person about his or her feelings of attraction, without, of course, intending to act on them. Not so. Recall that the feelings may be in large part biochemical, and if they are not acted upon they will usually vanish quite quickly.

Bill, a recovering alcoholic and traveling consultant, tells of "almost falling in love with" Sharon, a nurse at a hospital hundreds of miles from home. His travel took him there often, but he had yet to share his feelings with the nurse. He was happily married and had no desire to get involved with someone else. "But," he said, "I thought she had a right to know how I felt, you know, to clear the air. What I was really doing, I can see now, was just checking her out. I'd share what I felt, and if she didn't respond favorably, it would just be conversation. If, on the other hand, she had the same feelings, let the games begin!

"Anyway, I got her on the phone, on the company dime, of course, and was about to spill my guts when she began with some weirdo talk about astrologers and fortune tellers, major California stuff, really far out. I was really turned off. The bubble burst. I made up some phony reasons for the call and basically haven't thought of her since. But, if I'd shared what I wanted to, who knows what disaster would have followed? Sometimes the Higher Power has to watch me pretty closely!"

No one is *required* to share every emotion with everyone. Certainly, a sensible person should clue his or her sponsor in about such things, but it need not go further. If the potential relationship has real possibilities later on, it will happen when the time is right.

SHARE WITH A SPONSOR

A good sponsor can keep sponsees on track, spot the rationalizing and minimizing, help with the pain of recovery. A good sponsor can handle a Thirteenth Step crisis. But if a sponsor is uncomfortable about dealing with such issues, a second trusted person should be consulted.

When Wanda told her sponsor, Martha, that she was about to sleep with Joe, a married man in her home AA group, Martha didn't bat an eye.

"I told Wanda to think it through," Martha chuckled. "I said, 'Okay now, you're both married—right? So you'll need to set this up in the daytime—right? And you'll have to go to a motel. You don't have much spare cash, so it'll have to be a cheap one, like the Lakeside, you know, down near the railroad tracks, just past the landfill. Okay, so you get there and Joe pays the bill in advance. You park a little way off, so no one will spot your cars. Now you're in the room. I suppose you'll have to get undressed. Now, Joe's kind of on the heavy side, and well, I wonder if he wears those boxer shorts? Or maybe he can cover that gut in some other way. Oh, and there's birth control and AIDS to think about too. Even if you're on the Pill, you'd better go to a drugstore and get some condoms. What kind do you think he likes? Oh, and another thing. . ."

Wanda and Joe remain good friends, but there was no affair.

A sponsor will be a good listener, unshockable, and hopefully have a great sense of humor—and timing. Sponsors like Martha may be hard to find, but they're there. It's never too late to find a sponsor.

THE NO-CONTACT CONTRACT

If the worst has happened and a Thirteenth Step is in progress, ending it will mean taking certain steps.

First, meet privately with the sponsor to assess the situation. It's generally best to have no contact whatsoever with the "Thirteenth Step Squeeze" for a specific period of time; long enough to allow clarity to emerge regarding the relationship. This means, no matter how painful (and it *will* be painful):

- no face-to-face meetings
- no phone calls
- no letters, cards, or notes
- no messages through mutual friends

This may seem absolutely cruel and heartless, but the chemistry of the Thirteenth Step can be so powerful that little else can stop it.

The anguished lover may say to the sponsor or other trusted AA friend: "Why don't you trust me? Why? After all, I *am* an adult, and I've been sober almost six months!"

A sponsor could answer: "I do trust you, but I don't trust your *disease.* Nor do I trust what's happening to you now. I've been through the Thirteenth Step myself. Let me share my experience with you."

It's also important that the break, however short or long, is clear and without exception. The sponsee may ask, "What if I see him at an AA meeting?" The sponsor should answer, "Be polite, but do not engage in any lengthy conversation." There should be no need for extended and/or frequent explanations of the situation. One face-to-face explanation, clearly done, will always suffice. If the sponsee continues to be upset, the answer is more AA meetings, helping others, and venting those feelings with a sponsor and with good friends.

KEEP SPONSORS OUT OF THE MIDDLE

As the two individuals go their separate ways, one or both may attempt to prolong the situation by using a sponsor or some other AA member as a messenger service.

This can be staged. Carol says to Janie: "Hi, Janie, glad you could chair the meeting tonight. Oh, and by the way, you haven't seen old Fred, you know, my 'almost' guy?"

The game is on. Janie meets Fred the next day. He casually asks about Carol. Janie tells Fred not to worry, that Carol is fine and wishes him well; in fact, she misses him.

"How much?" asks Fred. If Janie answers, she's playing right into it; if she doesn't, she's a jerk and maybe even a home-wrecker, since Carol and Fred had been planning to move in together.

Stay out of it. Simple, direct answers to both parties will suffice. Janie could say: "I'm sorry Carol, but we agreed to keep me out of the middle. If Fred dies or wins the lottery, I'm sure you'll hear about it. I know it's painful, but you're doing so well I'd hate to see you take a step back."

THE ONE-YEAR RULE

AA wisdom has long suggested that recovering alcoholics should wait until they have been clean and sober for one year before making any major decisions. This includes starting any important new relationship. But even then, a determined Thirteenth Stepper can cause trouble. The more predatory ones are aware of the AA "one-year rule" and may even mark their calendars.

Holly was sober exactly one year when Jay, the guru of her home AA group, moved in for the Thirteenth Step kill.

Jay had been sober for ten years. He was fifteen years older than anyone else in the group, and was sponsoring quite a few of the young men. No one seemed to notice that he had no sponsor. Jay had heard Holly tell her friends that her sponsor had warned her to stay out of relationships for at least a year. The night of Holly's first anniversary, Jay gave her a long hug and asked in a paternal tone if he could give her a lift home. Holly accepted happily; she usually took the city bus.

Jay was married to his fourth wife. He told Holly that his wife didn't understand him the way AA people did. He was a traveling salesman who spent most weeknights on the road. He couldn't get to many meetings out of town. Would Holly object to his calling her sometimes? From his hotel room? For a little AA conversation?

One ride home led to another. Soon Holly invited Jay up to her apartment for coffee. Shortly after that he kissed her in a paternal fashion. Then in a nonpaternal fashion. Before Holly knew it, she was involved in a full-blown Thirteenth Step affair.

She was uncomfortable when Jay wouldn't let her tell anyone about their romance. All his reasons for secrecy seemed flimsy to her, but she was so dazzled by him, and he'd been sober so long, that she figured he must know best. He somehow convinced her that the secrecy was to protect *her,* and her sobriety.

Now Holly felt uncomfortable at meetings of their home group. She disliked pretending that there was nothing special between Jay and her. Did anyone guess? she wondered. Couldn't they *see* that the whole room lit up for her when he came through the door? That there was a shimmer around him when he arrived? That the meeting was a washout if he didn't come?

Once or twice a week, Holly began taking a train after work to meet Jay at motels an hour or more from the city. Early the next morning, she would take a train back. Jay never bought her a real meal. She would eat on the train, or she would skip dinner. She realized that he was sneaking her into his hotel rooms on his business account, that their "dates" weren't costing him one cent.

He began to manipulate her life, including her AA life, by persuading her to join him out of town on nights that her home group met; asking her to stay home for his phone calls instead of hanging out with her former group of single AA friends. Because she couldn't tell them the truth, a few of them asked her why she was withdrawing from AA.

Jay became more and more possessive, even following Holly to different cities when she visited family and friends, claiming that he had business there. But whenever she mentioned divorce, he would say, "Not now, darling. Be patient."

After six months of this, Holly sought professional help. Her therapist advised her to stop the affair immediately. For the first week, she wanted desperately to get drunk, but she didn't. She felt as if she were having a nervous breakdown, but she didn't. She forced herself to go to meetings every night, to work the Steps, and to socialize with her AA friends. She got a new sponsor and told her everything. She refused further contact with Jay.

Some months later, Holly noticed Jay congratulating another young woman on the night of her first anniversary. She zipped over in time to hear Jay offer the woman a ride home. "Sorry, Jay," Holly said sweetly. "She's coming out for ice cream with our whole gang."

Newcomers to AA should try to understand that the intention of the one-year rule is to offer one of the most important elements needed for recovery from chemical dependency: time. Time to grow, time to think, time to discover self-identity, time to heal. If recovering people are involved in a heavy relationship and/or other major changes, they won't get that time, and disaster is likely to follow. Whether the concept should *always* be followed and *always* take one year or more is up to the individual, but people find it helpful to honor the general principle of time.

Some things cannot wait. For example, if serious abuse issues emerge, they may have to be addressed sooner. If there is a violent relationship, a job that is very hazardous for recovery, or some similar situation, there may need to be a quick change. It always goes back to the AA Program and the sponsor. Hence the Program slogan so many newcomers dislike: "Give time time," or a south Florida variation, "Time takes time."

No Thirteenth Step situation will outlast a good sponsor, a strong home AA group, an equally strong and supportive same-gender AA group, and, above all, not picking up a drink—and time.

Chapter 6
Conclusion: More Eggs

*Life takes on new meaning in AA. To watch people
recover, to see them help others, to watch loneliness
vanish, to see a fellowship grow up about you, to have a
host of friends—this is an experience not to be missed.*

—*Alcoholics Anonymous,* p. 89

There is almost nothing more wonderful than romantic love.
We all know how special a certain face can look in moon-
light reflected from a shimmering sea, and we know how
good a special voice can sound on the telephone from far
away. And all those other corny, embarrassing things no one
wants to admit. We do "need the eggs," and at the right time
and in the right place with the right person, they can be fan-
tastic.

Jose and Francesca have been in recovery almost thirty
years. They met in AA twenty-five or so years ago; their
spouses had both passed away and loving AA friends had carried them through their separate griefs. They buddied
around together for many years until a fellow AA suggested,
"You guys sort of look right together. You ought to do something about that." They were married in two weeks and have
been together ever since. Their recoveries and their marriage have benefited people all up and down the East Coast
as they travel and speak at meetings, sharing the message
that "yes, there *is* life after recovery." And to show that they're
not letting age hinder their lifestyle, Francesca, who is near
seventy, took swimming lessons this summer so that she can
swim with her grandchildren!

41

Another happy story . . .

Ralph, fifteen years sober, had watched his wife drive away for the last time shortly after his company cut him from the job he thought he'd have for the rest of his life. Alice was a few years sober and really ready for a relationship, but prospects seemed nonexistent. She had been divorced for more than ten years. In the final act of letting go, she went to court and took back her maiden name, ready to face living alone. Until then, she'd always expected to remarry.

That week, Alice went to her home AA group and heard Ralph share his marital disaster. They did not fall into one another's arms, but within weeks they had their first "date"—going to a meeting and having coffee afterwards. They became friends, and shared their interests in dogs, the beach, the AA Program, and spirituality. A year or so later they were married, flanked by their sponsors and a host of Program people mixed in with family and a few others.

These are two stories of real people (names changed) who met in recovery and took their recoveries *to* each other rather than *from* each other. If partners bring recovery *to* one another, their recoveries are beautifully enhanced. But, if they try to take recover *from* one another, the relationship—and recoveries— suffer.

As long as two people concentrate on the first Twelve Steps, they should not have to worry about the Thirteenth.

The rewards? Always first and foremost: sobriety. Also, the wonder of sober sex, the return of self-esteem, the power of shared AA spirituality, and the sheer delight of being there to give a loved one his or her annual medallion and anniversary cake for another year of grateful sobriety.

Step Thirteen often appears in beautiful clothing and speaks with soft, seductive tones, tempting AA members with offers of escape from current, and perhaps harsh, reality. But, through trust in recovering friends, in the AA Program, and in a Power greater than ourselves, recovering people can find romance safely and joyfully, at a time and place that is *appropriate*.

You will surely meet some of us as you trudge the road of Happy Destiny.
—*Alcoholics Anonymous*, p. 164

Prayers for Recovering People

FOR A NEW RELATIONSHIP

First, as a way to let go of a new relationship and not force an outcome:

"God, take this relationship and let it become whatever You want it to be. I invite You into my day. Amen."

THE MARRIAGE PRAYER

"God, Your greatest gift to us is the gift of relationships, our relationship to You and to each other. We freely place our relationship in Your hands, knowing that in so doing, You will always give it back to us. Thus blessed and daily reminded, we go from here to do Your bidding and to return to Your care again this night. Amen."

Where to Get Help

The first and best line of defense in preventing and dealing with the Thirteenth Step is a caring home group, along with a good sponsor. However, additional help is often vital when other problems, such as sex addiction, serious depression, a history of physical or sexual abuse, or other addictions are present.

The following are suggested avenues for help:

Sex Addicts Anonymous
P.O. Box 3038
Minneapolis, MN 55403
Phone: 612/871-1520

Sex and Love Addicts Anonymous
Augustine Fellowship
P.O. Box 119
New Town Branch
Boston, MA 02258
Phone: 617/332-1845

Sexaholics Anonymous
P.O. Box 300
Simi Valley, CA 93062
Phone: 805/581-3343

S-Anon
P.O. Box 5117
Sherman Oaks, CA 91413
Phone: 818/990-6910

Sexual Compulsives Anonymous
(SCA East Coast)
P.O. Box 1585
Old Chelsea Station
New York, NY 10011
Phone: 212/439-1123

Sexual Compulsives Anonymous
(SCA West Coast)
4391 Sunset Blvd., No. 520
Los Angeles, CA 90029
Phone: 213/859-5585

National Council on Sexual
Addiction
P.O. Box 3006
Boulder, CO 80307
Phone: 303/494-5550

Codependents of Sex Addicts
(COSA)
P.O. Box 14537
Minneapolis, MN 55414
Phone: 612/539-6904

Adult Children of Sexually
Dysfunctional Families
P.O. Box 8084
Lake Street Station
110 East 31st Street
Minneapolis, MN 55408

Codependents Anonymous
(CODA)
P.O. Box 33577
Phoenix, AZ 85067-3577
Phone: 602/277-7991

Alcoholics Anonymous (AA)
P.O. Box 459
Grand Central Station
New York, NY 10163
Phone: 212/686-1100

Al-Anon Family Groups
P.O. Box 862
Midtown Station
New York, NY 10018-0862
Phone: 212/302-7240

Adult Children of Alcoholics
(ACoA)
Central Service Board
P.O. Box 3216
2522 W. Sepulveda Blvd., Suite
200
Torrance, CA 90505
Phone: 213/534-1815

Golden Valley Institute for
Behavioral Medicine
4101 Golden Valley Road
Golden Valley, MN 55422
Phone: 1-800/321-2273
612/520-1077

Narcotics Anonymous
P.O. Box 9999
Van Nuys, CA 91409
Phone: 818/780-3951

Cocaine Anonymous
P.O. Box 1367
Culver City, CA 90232
Phone: 213/559-5833

For specific help with relationships, check with a local addiction center or council on alcoholism. Remember that not all addiction experts know and understand relationship addiction or sex addiction.

If finances are an issue, a local community agency may help, and there are also private agencies, such as Catholic Charities or Lutheran Social Services, which accept clients on a "sliding scale" basis.

Suggested Reading

ALCOHOLICS ANONYMOUS

Alcoholics Anonymous ("Big Book") 3rd ed. New York: AA World Services, 1939, 1976.

Living Sober. New York: AA World Services, 1975.

Questions and Answers on Sponsorship (pamphlet). New York: AA World Services, 1983.

The AA Way of Life—a reader by Bill. New York: AA World Services, 1967.

Twelve Steps and Twelve Traditions ("12 and 12"). New York: AA World Services, 1952, 1953.

AA literature may be purchased through local Alcoholics Anonymous offices, or ordered from the General Service Office of AA, Box 459, Grand Central Station, New York, NY 10163. Some titles are also available through CompCare Publishers.

OTHER SOURCES

Baudhuin, John. *Now about Sex* (pamphlet). Center City, Minn.: Hazelden Foundation, 1983.

Bissell, LeClair, M.D., and James E. Royce, S.J. *Ethics for Addiction Professionals.* Center City, Minn.: Hazelden Foundation, 1987.

Carnes, Patrick, Ph.D. *Contrary to Love—Helping the Sexual Addict.* Minneapolis: CompCare Publishers, 1989.

Carnes, Patrick, Ph.D. *Out of the Shadows—Understanding Sexual Addiction.* Minneapolis: CompCare Publishers, 1983.

Cohen, Sidney, M.D. *The Chemical Brain—The Neurochemistry of Addictive Disorders.* Minneapolis: CompCare Publishers, 1988.

Good News Bible. New York: American Bible Society, 1976.

Hope and Recovery—A Twelve Step Guide for Healing from Compulsive Sexual Behavior. Minneapolis: CompCare Publishers, 1987.

Page, Susan. *If I'm So Wonderful, Why Am I Still Single?* New York: Bantam Books, 1990.

Peck, M. Scott, M.D. *The Road Less Traveled.* New York: Simon and Schuster, 1978.

Part Two

Romantic Relationship Inventory

Romantic Relationship Inventory with Sample Answers

"We got this all down on paper and looked at it."
—*Alcoholics Anonymous,* p. 69.

The concept of taking stock of ourselves is a basic component to many plans of personal growth, going back to ancient times, when the hero wandered out into the desert to find himself. In the Twelve Steps, we find the concept in Steps Four and Eight, and in Step Ten. The founders of the AA Program must have thought it important to get things down on paper and look at them. Only if we know what is wrong can we do anything about it. Santayana said that if we cannot remember the past, we are condemned to repeat it.

In the spirit of the "fearless and searching inventory" recommended by AA, this Relationship Inventory is suggested.

The inventory is divided into three parts: Relationship Attitudes, Relationship History, and Relationship Analysis. The guidelines and categories set down are not absolute; feel free to add your own ideas. This inventory is best done in private. Afterwards, the "exact nature" of the discoveries should be shared with a sponsor and any other trusted confidant(e), such as a clergy-person or therapist. The inventory should not be shared with a spouse or significant other.

The inventory appears first with sample entries to suggest how the inventory should be done. After that, the inventory is reprinted with enough blank space so that the reader may use this book to fill it out.

The most important part of any inventory, of course, is the action taken afterwards. Trends, issues, painful secrets, joyful triumphs—all of these results may require additional work with a sponsor or therapist. The results of that work, of course, will be worth it. "We will be amazed before we are halfway through," AA's "Big Book" promises us on page 83. And on page 84: "Are these extravagant promises? We think not. They will always materialize if we work for them."

I. RELATIONSHIP ATTITUDES

This part of the Relationship Inventory will help us discover how we look at relationships; and how we feel about them. While doing this part of the inventory, it is not important to remember exact dates and situations, but it will be important to be as honest as possible and to become aware of what we generally expect in a relationship. Some examples follow (written from the viewpoint of a woman).

A. Briefly describe what you believe an ideal romantic relationship should be like.

We would meet unexpectedly, perhaps through work. There would be late phone calls, letters, flowers, the works.

B. How do you know when you're "in love"? List at least three signs which fit for you.

Can't think, eat, or sleep without thinking of the person. Care and concern, desire to be with person as often as possible.

C. Describe your ideal romance mate. (Pretend that frogs *could* be turned into princes or princesses!) Be sure to include the following categories, and add more if you like.

- appearance
  lean, angular, piercing eyes, serious look but bright smile. Sharp dresser.

- job/career
  a professional—doctor, lawyer.

- family background
  from a large family, no CoAs (children of alcoholics) please!

- cultural/ethnic background
  same as mine—Eastern European.

- religion (If he or she doesn't have to be a certain religion, what kind of spiritual values would you want?)
  would be easier if Catholic, but this isn't big issue.

- leisure preferences (What kinds of things would he or she do for fun? How would you spend weekends? Where would you go for vacations? Would you expect leisure time for yourself?)
  swim, ski, go on cruises—I also want my own time.

- sexuality (What would you expect sexually? How often, who initiates it, etc.?)
  should be exciting, stimulating, romantic—no weird stuff.

- lifestyle (Would he or she be a city person, a country person, live in a house or apartment/condo? Would the place be formal or informal, neat as a pin or casual? Would you share all household chores equally, or divide them?)
  would prefer a city person used to a fast pace— place would be nice but modern and relaxed— no dark woods or oriental rugs. I'd do all the cooking but he should help with dishes, and take care of the garbage and cars and yard.

- sense of humor (Is this important, and if so, how?)
not that important—wouldn't want some come-dian, but should be able to have fun.

- attitudes about money (Do you always pay bills promptly and save for a rainy day? Or figure that your finances will work themselves out somehow? Would you want your ideal romantic love to take care of you financially? Or would you take care of him or her? Who would be primarily in charge of the money? You? Or he or she?)
I can never balance my checkbook—maybe I should look for a single CPA! Still, I work and would want to have my own money.

- other (List anything else you think is vital for your ideal partner.)
must have good attitude about recovery. I need meetings and time with my sponsor and AA friends. I don't want an AA person, though I'd consider it. He'd have to be at least a few years along in recovery.

D.   Describe your *first ever* romantic or love relationship:

- both of your ages
I was 14, he was 19—my parents went crazy.

- how you met
at a dance.

- who initiated or started the relationship?
he did.

- who ended the relationship?
he did.

- type of person
always in trouble—in fact, he ended the relationship because he went to jail. I wrote to him for a while. Then he told me to stop.

- were either of you an alcoholic, other chemical dependent, or child of an alcoholic? If so, describe.
  both chemically dependent.

- any violent or coercive incidents? If so, describe.
  he got angry and scared me, but was never physically abusive.

- sexual involvement, if any
  right from the start. Toward the end, we were more into drugs than sex.

- drinking/drug-taking together? Separately?
  he started me on drugs—we used to do lines together, smoke pot, and drink.

II. RELATIONSHIP HISTORY

In this part of the relationship inventory, the focus is on specific relationships. By writing the history, we will identify which relationships, if acted upon, will help us experience smoother sailing in the future. Use the relationships chart suggested here, or your own if you wish. And remember once more that a sponsor can be very helpful in supporting you through this difficult process. Some examples follow in chart form. End this history with your most recent or current relationship.

First name last initial	Length of relationship (days, months, years)	Wed/Unwed[1]	Marriage[2]	Nature of relationship[3]
1. *Zack D.*	*3 years; never made any real commitment*	*both single*	*never married*	*boyfriend*
2. *George D.*	*off and on—saw him when Zack wasn't around (Zack's brother)*			
3. *Jim Z.*	*1 month; ran away together—parents got us back*	*unwed*	*no marriage*	
4. *Chip M.*	*6 months; Chip was boring—college student*	*unwed*	*no marriage*	*boyfriend*
5. *unknown*	*1 day*	*unknown*	*no*	*one-night stand*
6. *Ed*	*5 years*	*he was married; got a divorce*	*married 2 weeks after his divorce*	*sexual, then romantic; 1 child*
7. *George*	*3 months*	*saw him while married to Ed*	*never married*	*sexual*
8. *Francine*	*2 weeks*	*neither married*	*not possible*	*sexual*
9. *Carl*	*6 months*	*he was married*	*no*	*sexual, romantic*
10. *Mark*	*2 years—still with him*	*both single*	*engaged*	*friends, now sexual*

1. you were both single; one was single, one married; you were both married (to others).

2. resulted in marriage; did not result in marriage; married to each other now; married each other but now separated or divorced.

3. romantic; romantic and sexual; sexual; different sexual preferences.

Who started relationship?	Who ended relationship?	Were alcohol/other drugs involved? AA?	Physical/sexual abuse?	Who controlled it?	Other
Zack	me	yes	verbal abuse	he did	very jealous
George	me	yes	no	I did	very sneaky
Jim	me; his parents thought I was "good" for him!!	yes	verbal abuse	I did	
Chip	me	no	very little sex	I did	became an internist
he did	unknown	yes	maybe—can't recall, was in a black-out	I don't know	
I did	I did	not at first	no abuse	I did	I left him for someone else
I did	I did	yes	no abuse	I did	an addict
she did	I did	yes	she was very very jealous	she did—one reason why I left	experiment with a woman, didn't like it
I did	he did	no—I was in AA	no abuse	I did	he was much older
). I did	still together	no-I'm in AA, he's not alcoholic	no	we're still trying to decide (he usually has the remote control for the TV!)	hope to get my daughter back

III. RELATIONSHIP ANALYSIS

A. Now review the relationship chart and list any trends or common situations you notice.

I started most relationships, ended most of them—control issue—I need to run the show. Drinking/drugging led to more weird relationships, but first sober one was weird too. I didn't like the premed student because he was too tame.

B. List the most important things you have to offer in a relationship (at least four).

1. wisdom—I've learned a lot
2. cheerfulness—I don't get depressed easily
3. honesty
4. I'm still in good shape—I can be attractive

C. List the most important things you deserve in a relationship (at least three).

1. consideration
2. loyalty
3. fun—it should be fun to be with someone

D. What would you like most to change about yourself?

1. feel less guilt over the past
2. I'd like to lose ten pounds
3. I've already gotten rid of the gray!
4. more recovery time

E. What would you like to change about your current or next relationship?

I'd like him to be more decisive. I think I picked him because I could be in control. Now I want him to change!

Romantic Relationship Inventory Workbook

Now about sex. Many of us needed an overhauling there.

Alcoholics Anonymous, p. 68

The purpose of this inventory is to help us examine our relationships, particularly romantic or "love" relationships, in order to learn about our relationship patterns.

Then, with the help of a Higher Power, we hope to develop better relationships in the future.

In a romantic love relationship, we are infatuated, preoccupied with the loved one, sad when he or she is absent, and despondent if the relationship ends. While many become sexual, a relationship can be quite romantic and even troublesome without sex.

Some may find doing this inventory a painful or upsetting process, however necessary it may be. For that reason, it is best to do it with the support of a good sponsor and, in many cases, an understanding and competent therapist, who can help process the issues identified by the inventory.

We will begin this inventory by looking at relationships and our general wants and needs, focusing on attitudes and trends. Then we will inventory specific relationships. Many will find comfort and guidance through frequent discussions about this with a sponsor or trusted friend.

There are no right or wrong answers for this inventory. But we should be as honest as we can.

I. RELATIONSHIP ATTITUDES

This part of the Relationship Inventory will help us discover how we look at relationships and how we feel about them. While doing this part of the inventory, it is not important to remember exact dates and situations, but it will be important to be as honest as possible and to become aware of what we generally expect in a relationship. Some examples follow.

A.   Briefly describe what you believe an ideal romantic relationship should be like.

B. How do you know when you're "in love"? List at least three signs which fit for you.

C. Describe your ideal romance mate. (Pretend that frogs *could* be turned into princes or princesses!) Be sure to include the following categories, and add more if you like.

• appearance

• job/career

• family background

• cultural/ethnic background

- religion (If he or she doesn't have to be a certain religion, what kind of spiritual values would you want?)

- leisure preferences (What kinds of things would he or she do for fun? How would you spend weekends? Where would you go for vacations? Would you expect leisure time for yourself?)

- sexuality (What would you expect sexually? How often, who initiates it, etc.)

- lifestyle (Would he or she be a city person, a country person, live in a house or apartment/condo? Would the place be formal or informal, neat as a pin or casual? Would you share all household chores equally, or divide them?)

- sense of humor (Is this important, and if so, how?)

- attitudes about money (Do you always pay bills promptly and save for a rainy day? Or figure that your finances will work themselves out somehow? Would you want your ideal romantic love to take care of you financially? Or would you take care of him or her? Who would be primarily in charge of the money? You? Or he or she?)

- other (List anything else you think is vital for your ideal partner.)

- in a recovery program

D.   Describe your *first ever* romantic or love relationship:

• both of your ages

• how you met

• who initiated or started the relationship

• who ended the relationship

• type of person

• Were either of you an alcoholic, or other chemical dependent, or child of an alcoholic? If so, describe.

• Any violent or coercive incidents? If so, describe.

• sexual involvement, if any

• Who controlled the relationship?

II. RELATIONSHIP HISTORY

In this part of the relationship inventory, the focus is on specific relationships. By writing the history, we will identify which relationships, if acted upon, will help us experience smoother sailing in the future. Use the relationship chart on pages 72 and 73 or your own if you wish. And remember once more that a sponsor can be very helpful in supporting you through this difficult process. Some examples follow in chart form. End this history with your most recent or current relationship.

First name last initial	Length of relationship (days, months, years)	Wed/Unwed[1]	Marriage[2]	Nature of relationship[3]
1.				
2.				
3.				
4.				
5.				
6.				
7.				
8.				
9.				
10.				
11.				

1. you were both single; one was single, one married; you were both married (to others).

2. resulted in marriage; did not result in marriage; married to each other now; married each other but no separated or divorced.

3. romantic; romantic and sexual; sexual; different sexual preferences.

ho started it?	Who ended it?	Were alcohol/ other drugs involved? AA?	Physical/sexual abuse	Who controlled it?	Other
.					
.					
.					

III. RELATIONSHIP ANALYSIS

A.   Now review the relationship chart and list any trends or
common situations you notice.

B. List the most important things you have to offer in a relationship (at least four).

C. List the most important things you *deserve* in a relationship (at least three).

D.   What would you like most to change about yourself?

E. What would you like most to change about your current or *next* relationship?

This completes the romantic relationship inventory. Now that you've finished you should congratulate yourself; this can be a very difficult and painful task. As with the AA Fourth Step, this inventory, too, will take on a greater value if shared with another human being in the form of another Fifth Step, or a Tenth Step—whichever your sponsor recommends. Also, if you are currently seeing a therapist, you might wish to share this with him or her for further insight.

The most important part of the Relationship Inventory, however, is not what you have done so far, but how you will use what you have learned to shape a better future. May this book and this inventory add to the joy and wisdom of your continued journey down the "Road of Happy Destiny" promised by the recovery fellowship, and may you find the companionship you so richly deserve.

About the Author

John S. Baudhuin, M.A., C.C.D.P., has over twenty years' experience in the field of addiction and psychiatric health care. Currently Program Director of the Dual Diagnosis Unit of Savannas Hospital in Port St. Lucie, Florida, John has served as a counselor, consultant, and trainer throughout the United States. He worked with some of the first inpatient addiction treatment facilities, including the Johnson Institute's program at St. Mary's Rehabilitation Center in Minneapolis.

Born in Wisconsin, John Baudhuin earned his Bachelor of Arts Degree Magna Cum Laude from Augsburg College in Minneapolis. He later received a Master of Arts degree in counseling from the Goddard Graduate Program of Vermont College, Norwich University, in Montpelier, Vermont. He is a Certified Chemical Dependency Practitioner, and he also served as an assisting clergyman for twelve years.

Other publications by John Baudhuin include *Living Longer, Living Better* (Winston Press); Hazelden pamphlets *Now about Sex, The Eleventh Step,* and *What Is Chemical Dependency?;* and many other articles, books, and pamphlets.

John lives in the Treasure Coast area of South Florida with his wife, Ruth Mary, and their Afghan hound, Balthazar.

Books on Twelve Step Recovery from CompCare Publishers

A Day at a Time. This classic little book of daily messages, now with a million in print, is available in three styles:
00018, 370 pages, rust hardcover
00075, 370 pages, gift edition, padded hardcover in gold box
03814, 365 pages, paperback

A Gentle Path through the Twelve Steps, *A Guidebook for All People in the Process of Recovery,* Patrick Carnes, Ph.D. Over 40 exercises, inventories, guided reflections help readers understand their own addiction/sobriety issues. 03731, 250 pages, paperback

God Grant Me the Laughter, *A Treasury of Twelve Step Humor,* Ed F. A collection of cartoons, quotes, and asides capture the relief and joy of recovery. 03764, 200 pages, paperback

The Serenity Prayer, *What Do the Words Really Mean?* Gary L. Thoughtful interpretations deepen the meaning of this well-loved prayer. 06684, 16 pages, pocket-sized pamphlet

Sober but Stuck, *Obstacles Most Often Encountered That Keep Us from Growing in Sobriety,* Dan F. Heartening life stories of sober people dealing with the most often seen issues in recovery—fear of intimacy, need to control, fear of rejection, anxiety, loneliness, depression, feelings of inadequacy, resentments, financial insecurity, and more. 04267, 204 pages, paperback

Sparks of Sound, *Reflections on Wisdom Heard at Twelve Step Meetings.* Wisdom straight from the heart of Twelve Step meetings includes 90 topical reflections collected by an insightful—and grateful—old timer. 03296, 208 pages, paperback

Survival Handbook for the Newly Recovering, Scott Shepherd, Ph.D. This popular book, a vivid and easy-to-understand allegory, guides the newcomer through perils of low self-esteem, boredom, loneliness, resentment, depression. 03715, 70 pages, paperback

The Twelve Steps for Everyone, *Grateful Members of Emotional Health Anonymous (EHA).* This CompCare classic, now in a meditation-size format, is for anyone in any Twelve Step group. 03970, 365 pages, paperback

Wisdom to Recover By, *Study Topics for People Growing in Sobriety,* Cecil C. An AA's "wise old-timer" and author of *These Golden Years* in AA's "Big Book" explores the most talked about topics in recovery—anger, denial, spiritual living, and more. 00430, 150 pages, paperback

The Winner's Way, *A Beginners Guide to the Twelve Steps,* Carol Hegarty. Important concepts presented in simple language. 06254, 38 pages, pamphlet

Order Form

Order No.	Qty.	Title	Author	Unit Cost	Total
04341		Romantic Relationships in Recovery	Baudhuin, J., M.A.	$6.95	
00075		A Day at a Time – Gift Edition	Anonymous	$10.95	
03814		A Day at a Time – Paperback	Anonymous	$6.95	
03731		A Gentle Path	Carnes, P., Ph.D.	$10.95	
03764		God Grant Me the Laughter	Ed F.	$ 7.95	
06684		The Serenity Prayer	Gary L.	$1.25	
04267		Sober but Stuck	Dan F.	$9.95	
03296		Sparks of Sound	Grateful Member	$6.95	
03715		Survival Handbook	Shepherd, S.	$3.95	
03970		Twelve Steps for Everyone	Grateful Members	$6.95	
00430		Wisdom to Recover By	Cecil C.	$7.95	
06254		The Winner's Way	Hegarty, C.	$2.95	
			Subtotal		
			Shipping and Handling (see below)		
			Add your state's sales tax		
			TOTAL		

Send check or money order payable to CompCare Publishers. No cash or C.O.D.'s please. Quantity discounts available. Prices subject to change without notice.

SHIPPING/HANDLING CHARGES

Amount of Order	Shipping Charges
$0.00-$10.00	$2.50
$10.01-$25.00	$3.50
$25.01-$50.00	$4.00
$50.01-$75.00	$5.00

Send book(s) to:

Name _____

Address _____

City _____ State _____ Zip _____

☐ Check enclosed for $_____, payable to CompCare Publishers

☐ Charge to my credit card   ☐ Visa ☐ MasterCard ☐ Discover

Account # _____ Exp. date _____

Signature_____Daytime Phone _____

CompCare®
Publishers

2415 Annapolis Lane, Minneapolis, MN 55441
To order by phone call toll free (800) 328-3330.
In Minnesota (612) 559-4800